Mel Bay Presents
Celtic Music for Folk Harp

By Laurie Riley & Leslie McMichael

2 3 4 5 6 7 8 9 0

Visit us on the Web at http://www.melbay.com — E-mail us at email@melbay.com

Table of Contents

Introduction 6

Components of Celtic Style 7

Ornamentation 10

About the Notation 12

About the Left Hand 14

Tunes for Moderate Skill Level:

      I Lost My Love 16

      The Orange Rogue 18

      The Shearin's No For You 20

      Fairy Dance 22

      Little Bag of Praties 24

      Mairi's Wedding 26

      Kelvin Grove 28

      Uir-chill A' Chreagain 30

      The Cat's Jig 32

Tunes at Intermediate Level:

      Jock O'Hazeldean 34

      The Water is Wide 37

      The Ash Grove 40

      Maggie Pickens 42

      Blind Mary 44

      Tarmon's Polka 46

Tunes at Advanced Level:

Roslyn Castle 49

The Butterfly 53

Barrett's Hornpipe 56

The Galway Piper 58

Hieland Laddie 60

My Love She's But A Lassie Yet 62

The Music of Turlough O'Carolan 65

Some Tunes by Turlough O'Carolan

Morgan Meaghan 66

Charles O'Conor 69

Carolan's Draught 70

Kathleen Astor 72

The Wire Strung Harp 73

Some Tunes Arranged for Wire Strung Harp

Castle Kelly 74

Parson's Farewell 75

Return from Fingal 76

About the Authors

Laurie Riley

Laurie Riley is a well-known performer and teacher of the harp. She began her musical career at the age of ten, and mastered a number of other musical instruments and voice before taking up the harp.

Scottish and Irish ancestry gave Laurie her love of Celtic music. Having studied it extensively, she is considered an authority on the style and the techniques involved in playing this music on the harp. She teaches lessons, workshops, and master classes, and has written numerous articles for the Folk Harp Journal of the U.S., and for Harpa Magazine of Europe. She has written several books.

As a touring performer, Laurie travels throughout the U.S. and Canada. She plays neo-Celtic, wire-strung, and double-strung harps. She now performs with her husband, Michael MacBean, also a harper.

Laurie's recordings include: "Double Image," "Glenlivet," "Midwinter Celebration," "Castle Kelly," and "Flowers of Edinburgh."

Laurie can be contacted at Box 249, Vashon Island, WA 98070.

Leslie McMichael

Leslie McMichael feels lucky to be doing what she loves for a living. A graduate of Wellesley College, her musical pursuits include teaching, performance, recording and composition. In 1992, Leslie co-founded the Vashon Island Harp School with Laurie Riley and Michael MacBean. The school, located a short ferry ride from Seattle in Washington State, is dedicated to bringing harp players together and expanding the horizons of what harp music can be.

A long-time pedal harpist, Leslie enjoys sharing her background of classical music and technique with both folk and pedal harpists. She has received training in the Suzuki method for young harpists and now heads the harp department at the Suzuki Institute of Seattle, in addition to directing two other Suzuki programs in the greater Seattle area. At Vashon Island Harp School, Leslie has directed the adult and children's harp ensembles, introduced lever harpers to the joys of pedal harp and taught beginning improvisation and ensemble playing. She takes great delight in presenting harpists and harp music in unusual situations!

Leslie has served the harp community as both president and vice-president of the Seattle Chapter of the American Harp Society. She can be contacted at P.O. Box 2193, Vashon Island, WA 98070.

Introduction

Welcome to the world of the Celtic harp. This book is intended to be an introduction to a style of music which has a long and noble history that is inextricably intertwined with that of the ancient harp.

"Celtic" is a term which has been much discussed among musicians and historians; some say the word cannot be applied to music or even to a culture, and that the correct term is "Gaelic." However, since it is commonly used, suffice it to say that the term "Celtic" refers to the culture and music of Scotland, Ireland, Wales, Brittany, Cornwall, and the Isle of Mann.

A lifetime can be cheerfully spent exploring the vast repertoire of Celtic music. It is characterized by a rich variety of styles, only a few of which can be explored in any one tune book.

The tunes contained in this book were chosen for their playability on the folk harp as well as for ease of separating into categories of skill. They have been arranged in a variety of ways that are representative of both ancient and modern styles, and are suitable for all types of harps.

The music of the Celtic people tells their story. It is full of joy and tears, love and war, laughter and loss. It never fails to touch its players and listeners deeply. It is my hope you will enjoy playing Celtic music as much as I do.

The skill levels of the tunes in this book are moderate, intermediate, and advanced. Beginners may feel comfortable with the moderate tunes, but may wish to start with Mel Bay's *Basic Harp for Beginners* by Laurie Riley.

Components Of Celtic Style

There are specific components within the playing style of Celtic music that make it sound truly Celtic. Many of these subtle things are not written into the notation, but must be learned by listening to Celtic music played by those who grew up in the tradition or have at least learned it from someone who did.

Music is a language, and Celtic style is one of its dialects. One cannot learn a language on paper alone; because the pronunciations of words would never be heard and thus never correctly spoken. Likewise, in music, the inflections and subtleties of style must be heard to be correctly interpreted. Because a piece of music notation says a tune is "Irish," for instance, it does not mean it is going to sound Irish unless one knows the style from having listened to it enough to absorb it completely.

Therefore I recommend that you buy as many recordings of Celtic music as possible, by artists from Celtic countries or those who know the style. Listen to fiddlers, bagpipers, and flute players in particular, and don't ignore vocalists who sing with folk groups from Ireland, Scotland, Wales, Brittany, etc.

Here are some of the particulars regarding Celtic style that are important to know as you learn the tunes in this book:

MELODY / INTERVALS:

Many Celtic melodies start with a 5th or a 4th in the first two melody notes. (Example: The Ash Grove)

Celtic tunes are modal, not chromatic, except Welsh music (see below). If they have accidentals, it is usually because they have been "corrected" by the person who wrote them down, either recently or in the past. (Example: Carolan's Draught)

KEYS:

Most Celtic tunes are in the keys of D, G, their relative minors Bm or Em, and occasionally in C or its relative minor Am. The reason is that many Celtic instruments such as fiddles, concertinas, and flutes only play in those keys. Occasionally a piece written for certain types of bagpipes will be in a flat key.

PATTERNS:

Most Celtic tunes have repeating patterns, i.e.: AABB; or ABC, ABC; etc. (Examples: The Butterfly, 3 parts, AABBCC; Lost My Love, 2 parts, AABB)

Having played the parts in order all the way through, a tune is usually then repeated. There are exceptions to this rule, and of course, when playing solo, you may play it as many times as you wish, with variations of your choosing.

You will read in the section on Turlough O'Carolan that he was influenced by baroque music. He made his tunes more complicated and although they still include repetition, the parts are often much longer, sometimes up to 16 bars long. (Example: Morgan Meagan)

HOW TO TELL IRISH, SCOTTISH, WELSH, ETC., APART FROM EACH OTHER:

Although much Celtic music sounds similar, there are important differences between styles from country to country. In ancient times, many musicians studied in schools or with masters elsewhere; for instance, a Scottish harper might go to Ireland to study, and vice versa. Therefore it can sometimes be difficult to determine which country a tune is from, and indeed the same tune may exist in only slight variation in more than one culture. However, many tunes can be clearly distinguished as Irish, Scottish, etc., for the following reasons:

The Scottish Snap is typical of only Scottish music. It sounds a bit like a grace note occurring on a downbeat, whereas often grace notes in Irish music are not on "important" beats. (Example: Jock O'Hazeldean. This is a slow tune but there is a type of dance tune called "strathspey" in which snaps are commonly used as well.)

Welsh music is usually chromatic, while other Celtic music is modal. This is due to the loss of earlier Welsh music. (Exceptions include "Ash Grove," because it appears to be old.)

Breton music has Moorish and French influences which can readily be heard in the modes used.

Irish music, when it is not Americanized (like much of what we hear on St. Patrick's Day), is characterized by its ornamentation. You will notice ornaments in some of the tunes in this book. Please read the chapter on ornaments.

In the late 1800's, a revival of interest in Celtic culture took place in this country, and much of the harp music passed on to us from that era contains Victorian-sounding arrangements, characterized by full-sounding harmonies and accompaniments. Some of the tunes in this book reflect that style, which has come to be accepted as a tradition.

TYPES OF TUNES IN THIS BOOK:
Jigs: 6/8 time, lively
Slip Jigs: 9/8 time, lively
Reels: 4/4 time, lively

Airs: slow and moody, pretty
Waltzes: 3/4 time
Ballads: tunes with words that tell a story.

HARMONY:

Ancient Celtic music usually has open harmonies such as 5ths, 4ths, and octaves. In accompaniments (left hand), thirds are often not used, though in this book some of the arrangements are "updated" and do contain them.

WIRE, GUT OR NYLON-STRUNG HARPS:

The ancient Irish harps had wire strings. These harps had a long sustain and bell-like sound. The difference in technique and sound involved the use of fingernails, the use of sustain, the use of damping, and the ancient sparse harmonies. Scottish gut-strung harps, by comparison, have a short decay. Nylon strings are more recent and sound like a cross between the two. Many of the tunes in this book can be played on wire-strung harp, and the last three are specifically arranged for wire-strung harp, with damping indicated on the notation. (These three tunes appeared in my *Basic Harp for Beginners* but were not arranged for wire harp in that book.) All of the tunes in this book are suitable for gut or nylon-strung harps, but may be played on wire-strung harps when you are familiar with the damping techniques and left hand modifications that make good wire harp arrangements.

Ornamentation

Ornaments are the essence of Irish and Scottish music. An ornament is a note or series of notes played in addition to the melody notes, for the purpose of enhancing the melody or accenting certain parts of it. When played on the harp, they are usually played with the same hand that plays the melody. Ornamentation is rarely included in music notation, and it is assumed the player will add the ornaments of his or her choice. However, in this book, a few ornaments have been added to the notation for your convenience. You may use them or not as you choose. I recommend that you add your own wherever you like.

Ornamentation originated with ancient Celtic vocal music and with bagpipes. It is used in all Celtic instrumentation.

There is no set terminology for each type of ornament; every teacher has his or her own names for each different one. The terms I use are as follows:

Runs: a series of notes (three or more) ascending or descending, ending on the melody note (each note is played by a separate finger.) A run is not in chord form but uses the notes of the scale that fall within the range of the run, and each note is distinct. It is shorter than a glissando. (Glissandos are not considered appropriate in Celtic music.) Examples: gabC or cbA.

Thumb slides: sliding the thumb down two, three or four notes and ending on the melody note. This is another way to execute a run.

Grace note: a note occurring just before a melody note and played so quickly that it cannot be construed as part of the melody. It can be lower than or higher than the melody note, and is usually not more than a fifth away. Occasionally an octave will be used.

Trill: a series of rapidly repeated plucks on the same string. In Scottish music, a trill can precede a melody note, a fourth, fifth, or octave up. (i.e.: cccG.)

In both Irish and Scottish music a trill can occur on the melody note and take the place of the melody note by dividing it into three notes which together equal the time value of the melody note. (On the flute and the bagpipe a trill is actually a five-note roll or "cran," which can only be executed on a harp more slowly; therefore, when a faster roll is necessary, a trill works.)

Doubles: like a trill except only two notes repeated, rather than three or four.

Repeated doubles: (also known as tremolo) this ornament uses both hands, and is done on two consecutive notes in ascending or descending order. The thumb and index finger of the right hand play two notes (i.e.: dc), followed by the left hand playing the same two notes. This can be repeated as long as one wishes, for the purpose of accenting a certain part of a melody. Each note must have the same time value.

Doubled trill: same as a doubled trill except three ascending or descending notes are used.

Rolls: there are three types of rolls, shown here by example.

abaga   or   *abag*   or   *agab*   or   *abagab*

Rolls end on the melody note. They are done so quickly as to not interfere with the rhythm of the piece. The last example is rarely used.

Chordal ornaments: playing the ascending or descending notes of a chord and ending on the melody note, in quick succession.

Octaves: playing the melody in two octaves at once with the right hand while accompanying with the left.

Here's how ornaments look in the notation. Don't get them mixed up with crossovers and crossunders (see section titled "About the Notation"). Ornamental notes are written smaller than melody notes.

grace note   *run*   *trill*   *repeated double*   *roll*

About the Notation

You will notice that there are additions to the notation in this book that are not usually seen on notation meant for instruments other than harp. There are also a few things that pertain to the Celtic nature of the tunes.

As mentioned in the section on Celtic Style, these tunes have parts that are repeated or that are important to recognize because they each make a separate "statement." On the notation you will see symbols like this:

These simply mean part A, part B, and so on. These parts are repeated in a certain order, so please pay special attention to the repeat signs.

means this is the start of a section that will repeat once.

means this is the end of the repeated section; the first time you come to it you will repeat the entire section once.

If you ignore the repeat signs the melody will become less meaningful and hard for the listener to follow.

When you get to the end of a piece you may wish to play it again; most Celtic tunes are repeated in their entirety at least once. If you feel confident that you have the ability to do so (and it's easier than you may think!), you may play the tune with variations of your own the second time through.

Harp notation has not yet been standardized. The symbols explained below may differ from book to book.

On some tunes you will find fingering brackets. Along with the brackets are finger numbers. Each bracket indicates a group of notes that is to be fingered as indicated (finger 1 is the thumb, 2 is index, three is middle, and 4 is ring). In addition, these fingers must be placed on the strings IN ADVANCE of playing any of the notes in that group.

Brackets with fingerings look like this:

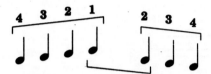

Both the fingering and the advance placement indicated by the brackets are VERY IMPORTANT. If you ignore them, you will never be able to play the tune comfortably, smoothly, or in a musical way. (It is possible to *sort of* play these tunes without proper fingering and placement, but *sort of* is all it will ever be.)

This symbol indicates a crossover or crossunder:

This symbol means roll your chord: ⦃

If you have not been exposed to the above concepts before, please get Mel Bay's *Basic Harp for Beginners* by Laurie Riley. It will help you acquire the skills necessary to play the tunes in this book.

About the Left Hand

Many of the left hand parts in these arrangements are best understood by looking first at the notation and recognizing the chordal nature of the notes you are to play.

For instance, a pattern like this

is really a chord broken into its component notes and played one at a time.

Left hand parts are seldom random. Even when you are playing single notes, those notes will probably relate to your right hand part in a way that can be recognized as chordal. For instance:

In this example, you can see that the intervals played with the left hand in the first measure form a chord with the corresponding notes of the right hand. In the second measure, the single notes of the left hand correspond with single notes on the right hand, both of which are members of a larger chord that is implied but not heard.

If you think of your left hand as playing chords that are preplaced whenever possible, you will simplify the playing and memorization of these pieces substantially.

I Lost My Love

Skill level: moderate

In this tune it is important to accent the first beat of each measure. (An accent means play the note louder but not longer). The full title of this Scottish tune is "I Lost My Love But I Didna' Know How."

(Source: Mickey Zekley)

I Lost My Love

Trad. Arr. Laurie Riley

The Orange Rogue

Skill level: moderate

Please notice that in part B, the left hand is written in treble clef.

This lovely tune has a strange name. I'm told it may refer to William of Orange, who was quite unpopular among the Irish. Why such a lovely tune should bear this name is a mystery.

(Source: Mickey Zekley)

The Orange Rogue

Trad. Arr. Laurie Riley

Play entire tune twice

The Shearin's No For You

Skill level: moderate

In pre-Christian times, springtime brought the celebration of fertility of both people and nature. With the arrival of Christianity, these rites were outlawed, later surviving only in remnants of their original form. Eventually, the springtime shearing of sheep was equated with a celebration of the new season, the warm weather, and the opportunity to be far from sight of any dwelling in the green grassy fields where the sheep were kept. Everyone knew that shearing was not the only activity young lads and lasses were engaging in, but it was probably considered futile to attempt to keep them occupied with sheep rather than with each other, as long as the sheep eventually got sheared.

(Source: Jean Farnworth)

Note: If your harp does not have enough bass strings to play this arrangement, you may play it one octave higher.

The Shearin's No For You

Trad. Arr. Laurie Riley

Repeat entire tune with your own variations

Fairy Dance

Skill level: moderate

This reel is known in several Celtic countries by different names. This is often the case with old tunes from any culture; you will find them in many musical and linguistic variations because they have been passed down through generations of musicians by ear.

(Source: Bill Ochs)

Fairy Dance

arr. Leslie McMichael

Little Bag Of Praties

Skill level: moderate

This Irish reel is dedicated to the humble but all-important *pratie* — the potato!

(Source: Bill Ochs)

Little Bag Of Praties

Trad. Arr. Leslie McMichael

Màiri's Wedding

Skill level: moderate

Usually played quickly, we found that this tune sounds very nice played moderately, with bagpipe-like harmonies.

(Source: Bill Ochs)

Màiri's Wedding

Trad. Scottish
Arr. Leslie McMichael

27

Kelvin Grove

Skill level: moderate

Once is not enough for this lyrical Scottish air. Do add your own variations.

Kelvin Grove

Trad. Arr. by Leslie McMichael

Uir-Chill A' Chreagáin

(the Clay of Kilcreagan)

Skill level : moderate

This slow air comes from the Gaelic vocal tradition.

Uir-Chill A' Chreagáin

Trad. Arr. Leslie McMichael

The Cat's Jig

Skill level: moderate

This extremely brief jig calls out for more variations of your own!

(Source: Bill Ochs)

The Cat's Jig

Trad. Irish
Arr. Leslie McMichael

2nd time 8va -

Jock O'Hazeldean

Skill level: intermediate

This tune should be repeated several times with variations of your own. You can create those variations by playing chords, by playing one note per measure, by making up another left-hand pattern, or by whatever means strikes your fancy. This is folk music, so you as the player are entitled to play it any way you like.

An important feature in this tune is the "Scottish Snap," an ornament which appears in measures 2, 10, and 26. Please see the chapter on ornamentation for instructions.

This is a Scottish ballad about the misery of arranged marriage. At least in this one, the true lovers find a way around the problem!

(Source: Jean Farnworth)

> Why weep you by the tide lady, why weep you by the tide
> I'll wed you to my eldest son and you shall be his bride
> And you shall be his bride, lady
> So comely to be seen
> But oh, she lets the tears run down for Jock O'Hazeldean
>
> A chain of gold you shall not lack, not braid to bind your hair
> Nor managed hawk nor mettled hound
> Nor palfrey fresh and fair
> But you the foremost of them all shall ride our forest green
> But oh, she lets the tears run down for Jock O'Hazeldean
>
> Now let this willful grief be done and dry your cheek so fair
> Young Frank is Lord of Errington and Chief of Langley Dale
> His step is first in peaceful hall, his sword in battle keen
> But still she lets the tears run down for Jock O'Hazeldean
>
> The church was decked by morningtide and taper glimmered fair
> The priest and groom await the bride and dame and knight were there
> They searched for her in bower and hall, the lady was na' seen
> She's over the border and awa' wi' Jock O'Hazeldean

Note: } means roll your chord

Jock O'Hazeldean

Trad. Arr. Laurie Riley

35

The Water is Wide

Skill level: intermediate

This is a ballad, a tune with words that tell a story.

> The water is wide, I cannot get o'er
> And neither have I wings to fly
> Give me a boat that will carry two
> And both shall row, my love and I
>
> There is a ship and she sails the sea
> She's loaded deep as deep can be
> But not as deep as the love I'm in
> I know not if I sink or swim
>
> I leaned my back against an oak
> Thinking it a trusty tree
> But first it bent and then it broke
> Just as my love proved false to me
>
> (repeat first verse)

Note: This symbol  indicates a rolled chord. (See Mel Bay's *Basic Harp for Beginners* by Laurie Riley)

The Water is Wide

Arr. Laurie Riley

39

The Ash Grove

Skill level: intermediate

This is a well-known Welsh air.

The Ash Grove

Arr. Laurie Riley

Maggie Pickens

Skill level: intermediate

In many of the tunes in this book, part *A* is played once through to the repeat sign, then repeated; likewise with *B*. This arrangement, however, skips the repeat signs entirely – instead having the four-measure statement of *A* followed by four measures of variation on *A*. (And the same with *B*!)

(Source: Bill Ochs)

Maggie Pickens

Trad. Irish
Arr. Leslie McMichael

Blind Mary

Skill level: intermediate

Mairi Dahl, the "Blind Mary" of the title, was a good friend of Turlough O'Carolan – small wonder, for the two had much in common. Each was an accomplished harper, and both had suffered loss of vision in childhood due to smallpox.

Blind Mary

O'Carolan
Arr. Leslie McMichael

45

Tarmon's Polka

Skill level: intermediate

Yes, there are Irish polkas! You'll notice a slightly different rhythmic accent than on, say, a Polish polka.

(Source: Bill Ochs)

Tarmon's Polka

Trad. Arr. Leslie McMichael

Roslyn Castle

Skill level: advanced

This Scottish tune is named for a castle in which it is said the once powerful Knights Templar hid from an angry Pope. It is located in a remote part of Scotland to which they retreated from all over Europe, leaving their vast land holdings which the Pope had decided should belong to the Church. Many who stayed behind were executed. At this castle, there is a chapel in which many carvings display symbols used by the Templars. It is here they apparently brought their considerable treasure; it is unknown what happened to it after that, but the Pope never found it.

(Source: Hamish Moore)

Roslyn Castle

Trad. Arr. Laurie Riley

The Butterfly

Skill level: advanced

This is a slip jig in 9/8 time.

Contrary to popular opinion, jigs should not be played at lightning speed. They are dance tunes and should be played no faster than a dancer can execute his or her steps. On a metronome, 116 or slightly faster is a suitable tempo, and certainly no faster than 132. Jigs and other dance tunes lose their lilt when played too quickly.

When learning dance tunes, learn them very slowly at first. Do not speed them up until you know them very, very well. Practicing fast will lead to sloppiness. Accuracy can only be gained by slow practice.

The Butterfly

Trad. Arr. Laurie Riley

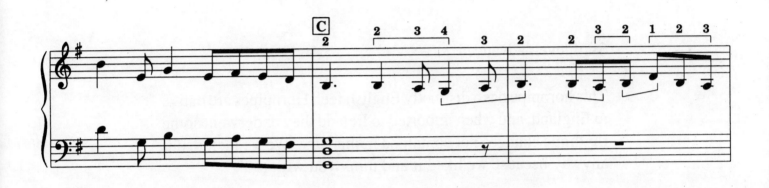

Repeat entire tune

Barrett's Hornpipe

Skill level: advanced

This hornpipe has a distinctly English feel. Hornpipes are native to England, and when imported to Ireland they underwent some rhythmic changes not contained in this tune. We've included it anyway because we liked it and think you will, too!

Barrett's Hornpipe

Trad. Arr. Leslie McMichael

o Play as a harmonic. Written where played, sounds one octave higher.

57

The Galway Piper

Skill level: advanced

This tune has an interesting title in that it reminds us that Ireland has bagpipes, too. We often think of the Scottish War Pipes, the ones you see in parades, but less often are treated to the lovely sound of the Uillean Pipes, which are not mouth-blown but are played by working a bellows with one elbow while also fingering the notes on the "chanter." The end of the chanter is open and for certain notes must be closed on the knee, so these pipes are played sitting down. (Many a good joke involves the image of Uillean pipers on parade.)

The Galway Piper

Trad. Arr. Leslie McMichael

Hieland Laddie

Skill level: advanced

Usually played as a march, this tune has a special quality when played moderately with these haunting harmonies.

Hieland Laddie

Trad. Arr. Leslie McMichael

My Love She's But A Lassie Yet

Skill level: advanced

This Scottish tune has the distinct feeling of a set dance. Picture square dancing, take away the big skirts and cowboy hats, add intricate foot movements, and you'll be playing for a set dance in no time!

My Love She's But A Lassie Yet

Trad. Scottish
Arr. Leslie McMichael

The Music Of Turlough O'Carolan

The following few tunes were written by a composer who is considered to have been Ireland's greatest. Around the late 1600's, Turlough O'Carolan wrote hundreds of tunes and played them on his wire-strung harp.

O'Carolan (sometimes referred to as Carolan) was blind from a childhood bout with smallpox. He made his living playing for noble families and composing music in honor of them. In exchange they offered their hospitality, sometimes for months at a time.

Often O'Carolan named his tunes after the patrons for whom they were written. Hence the names "Morgan Meaghan" and "Charles O'Conor." He often referred to the tunes as "planxtys," which means "in honor of."

The style in which he composed is distinctly different from older Irish tunes. The parts are longer before repeats occur, and they have a baroque flavor. This is due to his love of Italian Baroque music. His harp had no sharping levers, however, so he was limited to the diatonic scale. His music, as a result of that fact and of his lifelong exposure to pure traditional music, rendered his own compositions a lovely hybrid of two styles: baroque and Irish.

Only the melodies of his tunes were written down. We have little idea of how he used his left hand. The fanciful melodies seem to call for an active left hand, so I have arranged some of his tunes that way, such as in "Charles O'Conor" and "Carolan's Draught," but experimentation has shown me that he probably used simpler accompaniments, as in "Morgan Meagan."

Since they were written for the harp, the fingerings are delightfully logical for harpers to learn. They feel *good* to play.

Morgan Meaghan

Arr. Laurie Riley
Skill level: moderate

Repeat entire tune

Charles O'Conor

Arr. Laurie Riley
Skill level: intermediate

a trill may be substituted for these notes.

Repeat entire tune

69

Carolan's Draught

Arr. Laurie Riley
Skill level: advanced

flip C lever up with left hand now

flip C lever down with left hand now

Kathleen Astor

Arr. Laurie Riley
Source: Sheila Na Gig
Skill level: advanced

Repeat entire tune one octave higher

The Wire-Strung Harp

Although the following tunes can be played on any harp, my additions to the notation, indicating fingerings and damping, are specifically for wire-strung harp.

The wire-strung harp was used in Ireland until the early 1700's. It has a bell-like tone and a long sustain when plucked. Therefore, some notes must be damped (stopped) to keep the sound clear as subsequent notes are played.

In the notation you will see the symbol x appearing after certain notes, on the lines or spaces of notes that have been previously played. This means you are to damp (stop with a finger) the previously played note indicated by the x at the same time that you pluck the note that appears just before the x.

For example: in "Return from Fingal," the first note is E. The second note is D with an x on the E line. This means play the E, then play the D while damping the E. (If you damp a note before playing the next, you will get a staccato sound that is not appropriate. It is important to damp at the same time the next note is plucked.)

There are more advanced damping techniques. This is meant only as an introduction to the style.

Castle Kelly

Trad. Arr. Laurie Riley
Skill level: moderate

Repeat tune with your own variations

Parson's Farewell

This is an English tune that is
stylistically close to Celtic.

Trad. Arr. Laurie Riley
Skill level: advanced

Repeat entire tune

Return From Fingal

Trad. Arr. Laurie Riley
Skill level: Intermediate
Source: Ken Perlman

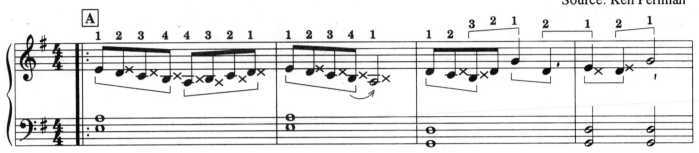

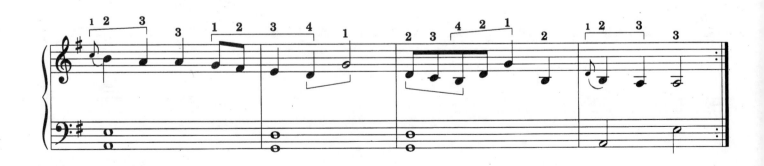